IN THE
TEMPLE OF SOLOMON
AND THE
TOMB OF CAIAPHAS

An Archaeological Exhibit in Honor of the Annual Meeting
of the Society of Biblical Literature, the American Academy of Religion
and the American Schools of Oriental Research
in Washington, DC, November 1993

presented by the

Biblical Archaeology Society
Washington, DC

publisher of

Biblical Archaeology Review

and

Bible Review

with artifacts loaned by

The Israel Museum and the Israel Antiquities Authority
Jerusalem

in cooperation with

The Smithsonian Institution
Washington, DC

In the Temple of
SOLOMON
and the Tomb of
CAIAPHAS

Hershel Shanks

BIBLICAL ARCHAEOLOGY SOCIETY
WASHINGTON, DC

In the Temple of Solomon and the Tomb of Caiaphas by Hershel Shanks
Catalog issued in conjunction with an archaeological exhibit presented by
the Biblical Archaeology Society
at the Smithsonian Institution, November 19-28, 1993
Library of Congress Catalog Card Number 93-073673

ISBN 1-880317-11-7

This catalog has been produced by the Biblical Archaeology Society
Hershel Shanks/editor
Suzanne F. Singer/managing editor
Steven Feldman/captions
Molly Dewsnap/copy editor
Emily Eisele/editorial assistant
Cheryl W. McGowan/administrative assistant
Susan Laden/publisher
Judy Wohlberg/production manager
Designed by Robert Sugar, AURAS Design, Washington DC

©1993 Biblical Archaeology Society
Washington, DC

TABLE OF CONTENTS

ACKNOWLEDGMENTS

We are especially grateful to Martin Weyl, Director of the Israel Museum, and Amir Drori, Director of the Israel Antiquities Authority, for their inspiration and their generosity, as explained more fully in the preface.

Similarly to Tom Freudenheim, Assistant Secretary for Arts and Humanities of the Smithsonian Institution, who provided the venue for this exhibit.

Without this trio of talented, can-do public servants, this exhibit would never have come into being.

Each of them is supported by a dedicated, imaginative and unfailingly pleasant staff who conscientiously performed the myriad of tasks that "made it happen":

At the Israel Museum:
Ya'akov Meshorer
Chief Curator of Archaeology

Michal Dayagi-Mendels
Curator of Israelite and Persian Periods

At the Israel Antiquities Authority:
Ruth Peled
Chief Curator

At the Smithsonian Institution:
Anne R. Gossett
Director, International Gallery

John Coppola
Director, Office of Exhibits Central

Diana Cohen
Editing

Eva MacIntyre
Design

Walter G. Sorrell
Fabrication and Installation

The Biblical Archaeology Society is also blessed with a wonderful staff, many of whom have made significant contributions to this exhibit: Suzanne Singer, Steven Feldman, Susan Laden, Margaret Owen, Judy Wohlberg, Molly Dewsnap, Emily Eisele and Cheryl McGowan.

The catalog text was reviewed by Ya'akov Meshorer, Michal Dayagi-Mendels, Zvi Greenhut and Ronny Reich (the former two from the Israel Museum and the latter two from the Israel Antiquities Authority), each of whom made valuable suggestions and saved us from error. The remaining errors are mine, probably because I failed to take some of their suggestions.

In heartfelt gratitude to all.

Hershel Shanks

DONORS IN SUPPORT OF THE EXHIBIT

Raising money, even for a good cause, is rarely pleasant. This exhibit was an exception.

To get me started and to raise my spirits, I went first to Shelby White and Leon Levy. To assure me that it could be done, I went next to Joan and Dick Scheuer. I then felt like a quarterback who had just been sent into the game by Knute Rockne (who is the most recent football coach I can name). After that, the rest was easy, especially because everyone who has contributed to this exhibit did so with enthusiasm and excitement. It is a pleasure to record their names:

Sponsors
Shelby White and Leon Levy

Benefactors
Maurice M. and Marilyn Cohen

Terrence A. and Ruth Elkes

Eugene M. and Emily Grant

Richard J. and Joan Scheuer

Patrons
Philip I. and Muriel Berman

Joshua B. and Lisa Bernstein

Norman and Diane Bernstein

CRESTAR Bank

R.R. Donnelley Magazine Group, Specialized Publishing Services

Joseph G. Hurley and Davia Solomon

Norma Kershaw

Manfred R. and Anne Lehmann

Morris Rodman

LIST OF ILLUSTRATIONS

PREFACE

THIS EXHIBIT CONSISTS OF ONLY TWO ITEMS—ONE TINY AND THE OTHER NOT LARGE. BUT they are among the most prized pieces on permanent display in the Israel Museum in Jerusalem. The brief, almost hushed descriptions provided by the curators of the Israel Museum for an American importation document related to this exhibit reflect their unique character in the world of Biblical archaeology:

1. "Inscribed ivory pomegranate from the second half of the 8th century B.C.E.,* apparently the only object known to have survived from Solomon's Temple in Jerusalem."

2. "A unique ossuary bearing the name 'Yehosef son of Caiaphas,' found in the family tomb of the Caiaphas clan, one of the prominent high priestly families of the Second Temple period, and may thus have belonged to Joseph Caiaphas, High Priest during the days of Jesus."

That these items have been permitted to leave Jerusalem—for the first and perhaps for the last time—is due to a combination of factors:

The first is the brevity of their sojourn in the nation's capital—a mere ten days.

The second is the special occasion.

The third is the unprecedented generosity, grounded in a courageous understanding of the importance of educational outreach, of the director of the Israel Museum, Martin Weyl, and the director of the Israel Antiquities Authority, Amir Drori. They, in turn, were supported and ably assisted by Ya'akov Meshorer, Chief Curator for Archaeology at the Israel Museum; Michal Dayagi-Mendels, Curator at the Israel Museum; and Ruth Peled, Chief Curator at the Israel Antiquities Authority. What a wonderful team to work with.

The genesis of this exhibit lies in the desire of the Biblical Archaeology Society to do something special for the largest and most important annual gathering of Bible scholars from all over the world, known as the Annual Meeting. Each year this joint meeting of three important American associations of scholars, the Society of Biblical Literature, the American Academy of Religion and the American Schools of Oriental

---

*B.C.E. (Before the Common Era) and C.E. (Common Era) are the alternative designations for B.C. and A.D. often used in scholarly literature.

Research, is held in a different city. And each year the number of American and foreign scholars who participate increases; in 1993, about 7,000 scholars will attend. For the first time in nearly 20 years, the meeting will be held in Washington, D.C., home of the Biblical Archaeology Society. Naturally, we wanted to mark the occasion. So I called my friend Martin Weyl to discuss the matter. It was he—I would never have had the chutzpah—who mentioned the possibility of lending us these two extraordinary artifacts for the short period of the Annual Meeting. I was absolutely incredulous—but, lawyer-like, I suppressed all emotion.

The inscribed ivory pomegranate belongs to the Israel Museum, so Martin could speak with some authority regarding this item, although the permission of the Antiquities Authority would still be required to permit it to leave the country. The Caiaphas ossuary, on the other hand, was excavated by the Antiquities Authority. Although it is on display at the Israel Museum, it belongs to the Antiquities Authority and therefore requires its agreement for any loan. With thoroughly unbureaucratic efficiency, the Antiquities Authority promptly gave its approval.

But we did not yet have an appropriate venue for the exhibit. Here too Martin Weyl came to the rescue, suggesting something I myself should have thought of—that I contact my friend and neighbor, Tom Freudenheim, Assistant Secretary for the Arts and Humanities at the Smithsonian Institution. Tom immediately suggested I talk with Anne Gossett, director of the Smithsonian's International Gallery, and in no time we arranged for the exhibit to be held at the S. Dillon Ripley Center of the Smithsonian Institution. Only then did I begin to believe that this exhibit would actually happen.

The Annual Meeting is being held on November 20 through November 23, 1993, ending the Tuesday before Thanksgiving. With uncharacteristic boldness, I proposed to Martin that we extend the exhibit until the Sunday after Thanksgiving to give Washingtonians and visitors a short opportunity to see these unique treasures. Both he and Amir Drori promptly agreed. And so this exhibit was born.

Hershel Shanks
President
Biblical Archaeology Society

THE IVORY
POMEGRANATE
FROM
SOLOMON'S
TEMPLE

Despite its diminutive size, this exquisitely carved ivory pomegranate looms large in the world of Biblical archaeology: It is believed to be the only surviving artifact from Solomon's Temple in Jerusalem. It probably served as the decorative head of a ceremonial scepter carried by the Temple priests more than 2,500 years ago. The pomegranate measures 1.68 inches high and .83 inches wide—the same dimensions as an actual pomegranate at this stage of development. Two petals and a portion of the ball have broken off. The artifact's importance is matched only by the mystery surrounding its discovery: No one knows when or where it was found or who sold it to the Israel Museum for $550,000. This exhibit is the first—and may well be the last—time this remarkable artifact has been permitted to leave Jerusalem.

A cross-section drawing of the ivory pomegranate shows that a small hole (6.5 mm. in diameter and 15 mm. deep) has been bored into the bottom. The hole indicates that the pomegranate had originally been placed atop a rod or, as one scholar has suggested, that it might have served as ornamentation on a Temple object.

To find a small ancient ivory pomegranate is exciting, but not surprising. Pomegranates were common symbols of fertility and fecundity in the ancient world because of their many seeds. Numerous references to pomegranates can be found in the Bible, in other ancient texts and in archaeological contexts.

BIBLICAL REFERENCES TO POMEGRANATES

POMEGRANATES ARE MENTIONED MORE THAN 30 TIMES IN THE HEBREW BIBLE—IN EXODUS, Numbers and Deuteronomy, in the Prophets, and of course in that great love song *Shir ha-Shirim*, the Song of Songs.

The Bible describes in great detail the vestments for the first high priest, Aaron, the brother of Moses. His robe is to be pure blue, decorated with pomegranates:

"On its hem make pomegranates of blue, purple, and crimson yarns, all around the hem, with bells of gold between them all around: a golden bell and a pomegranate, a golden bell and a pomegranate, all around the hem of the robe. Aaron shall wear it while officiating, so that the sound of it is heard when he comes into the sanctuary before the Lord" (Exodus 28:33-35; see also Exodus 39:22-26).

Pomegranates also decorated the capitals of the two freestanding bronze columns, named Boaz and Jachin, at the entrance to Solomon's Temple (1 Kings 7:42; 2 Chronicles 4:13). We are not sure how many pomegranates decorated these capitals. The sources just cited refer to 400. Other places mention 100 (2 Chronicles 3:16; Jeremiah 52:23), although these may not refer to all the pomegranates on these important capitals. In either case, it's a lot of pomegranates.

The pomegranate is one of the seven different species with which the Promised Land is blessed:

"For the Lord your God is bringing you into a good land, a land with streams and springs and fountains issuing from plain and hill; a land of wheat and barley, of vines, figs,

A symbol of fertility and fecundity in the ancient Near East, pomegranates are mentioned more than 30 times in the Hebrew Bible. "For the Lord your God is bringing you into a good land, a land with streams and springs and fountains issuing from plain and hill; a land of wheat and barley, of vines, figs, and pomegranates," says Deuteronomy 8:7-8. Pomegranates are shown here in flower, as a bud and as a mature fruit.

The quartet of artifacts on this and the opposite page are some of the many ancient objects depicting pomegranates. Shown above is a 13th-century B.C.E. pomegranate-shaped glass vase. At top on the next page is the 12th- or 11th-century B.C.E. Kibbutz Sasa kernos (named after the collective farm in northern Israel on which it was found); a globular ceramic pomegranate from the 11th or 10th century B.C.E. appears below it. Underneath that is a pomegranate at the center of a 9th-8th century B.C.E. platter measuring 7 inches in diameter, discovered at Tel Halif (modern Lahav) in the northern Negev. The objects on which pomegranates appear seem frequently to have been used in a cultic context. Kernoi are hollow clay rings about a foot in diameter from which various hollow objects sprout—a bird or other animal, a cup or other vessel, and the like. The Kibbutz Sasa kernos features a chalice, a bird and two pomegranates. Scholars speculate that kernoi were filled with a liquid (water or wine), shaken and then tipped to allow the liquid to pour out of the openings, in some unknown ritual.

and pomegranates, a land of olive trees and honey; a land where you may eat food without stint, where you will lack nothing; a land whose rocks are iron and from whose hills you can mine copper. When you have eaten your fill, give thanks to the Lord your God for the good land which He has given you" (Deuteronomy 8:7-10).

In the Song of Songs, a young woman invites her lover to make love to her under a pomegranate tree, perhaps to ensure fertility:

"I am my beloved's,
And his desire is for me.
Come, my beloved,
Let us go into the open;
Let us lodge among the henna shrubs.
Let us go early to the vineyards;
Let us see if the vine has flowered,
If its blossoms have opened,
If the pomegranates are in bloom"

Song of Songs 7:11-13.

In another passage from the Song of Songs, the pomegranate is a metaphor for a beautiful feminine brow. This time a man describes his beloved:

"Ah, you are fair, my darling,
Ah, you are fair.
Your eyes are like doves
Behind your veil.
Your hair is like a flock of goats
Streaming down Mount Gilead.
Your teeth are like a flock of ewes
Climbing up from the washing pool;
All of them bear twins,

And not one loses her young.
Your lips are like a crimson thread,
Your mouth is lovely.
Your brow behind your veil
[Gleams] like a pomegranate split open.
Your neck is like the Tower of David..."
Song of Songs 4:1-4

The pomegranate was just as important to other peoples who lived in the Fertile Crescent—Israel's neighbors and people who lived there before the Israelites—and their writings reflect this.

POMEGRANATES IN ARCHAEOLOGICAL CONTEXT

ARCHAEOLOGICAL FINDS CONFIRM THE PREVALENCE OF POMEGRANATES IN THE ANCIENT consciousness, especially in *Eretz Yisrael*, the Land of Israel. More than this, however, many of the finds suggest the use of the pomegranate in a religious context, one factor among several that must be considered in assessing the ivory pomegranate in this exhibit.

A number of ceramic pomegranates have been found in excavations in Israel, dating from the twelfth to the eighth century B.C.E. Scholars are not sure how they were used, but it seems they were employed in cultic rituals.

This is more explicit in the case of pomegranates found on *kernoi*. A *kernos* is a hollow clay ring about a foot in diameter from which various hollow objects sprout: a cup, other vessels, an animal, a bird—or a pomegranate. One of the most beautiful and most nearly complete *kernoi* is known as the Kibbutz Sasa *kernos*, named after the kibbutz in northern Israel where it was found. Four of the six objects that originally stood on the Kibbutz Sasa *kernos* have survived—a chalice, a bird and two pomegranates. The *kernos* was used in an obscure religious ritual. Apparently, some liquid (water or wine) was poured through orifices in the hollow objects and into the ring. The *kernos* was shaken, the liquid

Pomegranate-shaped pendants decorate the rim of a 13th-century B.C.E. bronze cult stand from Ugarit (Ras Shamra, along the Mediterranean coast of modern Syria). This stand supported a bowl or dish in which incense was probably burned. Similar in function was a 13th- or 14th-century B.C.E. bronze stand (far right) discovered in an unrobbed grave at Tel Nami (eight miles south of Haifa). The decorations at the top are pomegranates or, some have suggested, poppy seed pods.

The widespread popularity of pomegranates is further shown by a pair of gold earrings in the shape of pomegranate blossoms from Tel Nami. Similar pendants from 8th-century B.C.E. Megiddo, in northern Israel, have also been recovered.

was poured out and a benediction was recited. The Kibbutz Sasa *kernos* dates from around the 12th or 11th century B.C.E., the period when the Israelites were emerging in Canaan.

Another curious example of a ceramic pomegranate (p. 16) was found at Tel Halif, the site of modern-day Kibbutz Lahav, in the northern Negev. It is attached to the center of a platter and dates to the ninth-eighth centuries B.C.E. No one has yet explained how this platter was used, if it was used at all.

Pomegranates also decorated cult stands (p. 18). One of the most beautiful comes from Ugarit, an important 14th- and 13th-century B.C.E. city on the Mediterranean coast of modern Syria. The site, known in modern Arabic as Ras Shamra, has been intensively excavated, and gorgeous finds, including a unique cuneiform archive, have been recovered. The finds include a cultic tripod surmounted by a metal ring that once held a bowl or dish of some kind. A series of pomegranates hangs from the ring.

At Tel Nami, eight miles south of Haifa, excavators recently discovered several bronze incense burners, dating to the 14th or 13th century B.C.E. One of them—a four-footed stand (p. 18)—features "bells" hanging from its top. The bells represent either pomegranates or poppy seed pods.

Interestingly, two pomegranate pendants almost identical to those on the Ugarit tripod were found in Israelite Megiddo (eighth century B.C.E.).

Pomegranates were also popular decorations on Hebrew seals of the 8th and 7th centuries B.C.E. One of the most beautiful is the seal of Ḥananyahu son of 'Azaryahu.

During the Great Revolt against Rome (66-70 C.E.), which effectively ended with the destruction of the Second Temple, the Jews minted their own coins. Nationalist fervor is reflected on these coins in the use of the old Hebrew letters (paleo-Hebrew in scholarly jargon) that had not been in common use since the Babylonian Exile in the sixth century B.C.E. Reaching back for another ancient symbol, the Jews at the turn of the era also decorated their revolt coins with a cluster of pomegranates.

A ring of pomegranates encircles a 7th-century B.C.E. Hebrew seal belonging to one Hananyahu son of 'Azaryahu. Pomegranates were a widespread decorative motif on Hebrew seals of the eighth and seventh centuries B.C.E. At top is an impression of the seal; below, the seal itself.

"Jerusalem the Holy" says the inscription on a shekel coin from the First Jewish Revolt against Rome (66-70 C.E.). This coin was struck during the second year of the Revolt. Those who fought Rome deliberately sought to retrieve ancient Jewish symbols. This coin bears two such symbols: Its script is paleo-Hebrew, a script not in wide use for the previous 500 years; the second symbol, meant to recall ancient Hebrew splendor, is the cluster of pomegranates at center, a motif found on many coins dating to the Revolt.

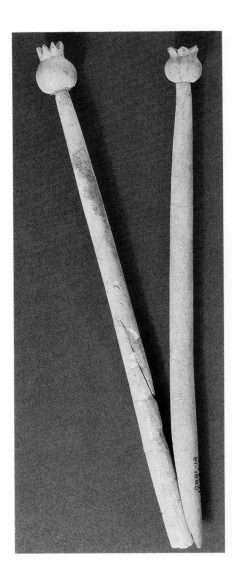

In short, the pomegranate was used as an important religious and national symbol for more than a thousand years.

The ivory pomegranate in this exhibit, however, had a function different from any of those listed above. It was very probably the head of a priestly scepter!

HOW WE KNOW THE IVORY POMEGRANATE WAS THE HEAD OF A PRIESTLY SCEPTER

ESTABLISHING THAT THE IVORY POMEGRANATE IN THIS EXHIBIT FUNCTIONED AS THE HEAD of a priestly scepter requires a close look at the object. Most people on first look doubt that this tiny object—just an inch and a half from top to bottom—could have been used in this way. But the evidence is overwhelming.

Most of us know pomegranates in their ripe form, ready to eat. At that stage the pomegranate is globular and much larger than the pomegranate in this exhibit. Examples of fully ripe pomegranates can be seen in several of the archaeological specimens already discussed.

The pomegranate in this exhibit is at an earlier stage, a mere bud. This too is common in other archaeological specimens. At this stage, the body resembles a small, gracefully designed oblong vase. In the pomegranate in this exhibit, the rounded body tapers toward the bottom. The neck is relatively long and narrow, sprouting into six petals— all realistic of an actual pomegranate at this stage in its development, down to the number of petals. In our example, however, two of the petals have been broken off. And one side of the grenade, as the body is called, has been destroyed.

The body is solid, but a small round hole (6.5 mm. in diameter and 15 mm. deep) has been carefully cut into the base (see drawing, p. 14). That hole is the first clue that the pomegranate once surmounted a scepter: A rod or shaft was inserted into this hole.

Frank Moore Cross of Harvard University has suggested that the ivory pomegranate could have acted as a finial on a small box or even on a piece of furniture, rather than as the head of a scepter. While this remains a possibility, the archaeological evidence strongly suggests that it was the head of a scepter. This evidence consists of several similar scepters that have been recovered, including some with pomegranate heads very much like the example here.

Pomegranate-headed scepters have been found at Kition and Enkomi on the island of Cyprus, as well as at several sites in Israel—Lachish, Achziv (excavated by Moshe Prausnitz) and, most recently, Tel Nami, where a splendid bronze example was found. The excavator of the bronze scepter, Michal Artzy of the University of Haifa, concludes that the tomb in which the scepter was found was that of a priest, as evidenced by other grave goods. It dates to the 13th century B.C.E. This tends to confirm that the scepter functioned in a religious context. Incidentally, Artzy also found another beautifully carved ivory scepter rod; unfortunately, the head of this rod did not survive.

The evidence thus far has established that our ivory pomegranate was the head of a scepter and that scepters of such small size—the rod was less than a foot long—were quite common. We might more easily liken it to a wand were it not for the association of wands with magicians and conjurers. The scepter was associated with authority and, as the evidence we have adduced suggests, was used in a religious context, probably in connection with some ritual.

But how can we connect this scepter with Solomon's Temple? This question leads us to the most extraordinary aspect of the ivory pomegranate.

THE INSCRIPTION

A UNIQUE INSCRIPTION CARVED IN ANCIENT HEBREW SCRIPT ENCIRCLES THE SHOULDER OF THE pomegranate. Fortunately, it is quite clear and easily read under a magnifying glass. All scholars who have looked at it agree on the letters.

Unfortunately, part of the inscription is missing, broken off with two of the petals and part of the grenade. This has given rise to some controversy: How should the mis-

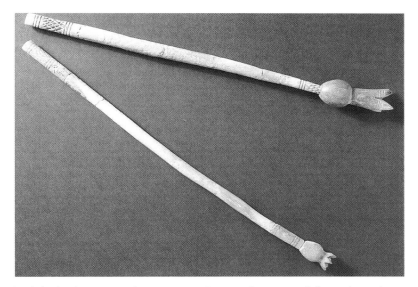

Symbols of authority, several ancient scepters have now been recovered, frequently in religious contexts. The pair above was excavated amid other cultic items in a 13th century B.C.E. Canaanite temple at Lachish. They provide the closest parallel to the pomegranate on display in this exhibit. Each made of ivory, the scepters consist of 9.5-inch-long rods topped by a pomegranate; the one at top is especially close in size and shape to our inscribed pomegranate and gives a good indication of how it might have looked in its original condition.

The trio of scepters in the center of the opposite page were discovered in two 13th-century B.C.E. graves at Tel Nami, just south of Haifa. Incised designs decorate the ivory of the the left-most scepter; unfortunately, the top was not recovered. The other two scepters are made of bronze and come from the same grave as the incense stand and the gold earrings shown on page 18. The scepter at center features a pomegranate decoration, while the ornament atop the other scepter may represent either a pomegranate or a poppy seed pod. Michal Artzy, Tel Nami's excavator, believes the grave held the remains of a priest who had been interred with the cultic implements he had used while carrying out his priestly functions.

At far left on the opposite page are two eighth-century B.C.E. ivory specimens from Achziv, a Phoenician site north of Haifa, excavated by Moshe Prausnitz. These finds strongly suggest that the inscribed pomegranate in this exhibit served as the top of a scepter.

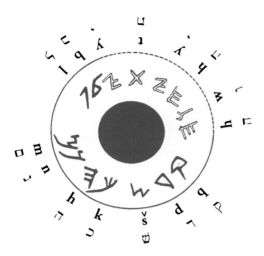

The pomegranate, opposite, viewed from above, shows its paleo-Hebrew letters still clearly visible around the shoulder. The drawing above indicates extant letters in black and restored letters in outline form (the dashed lines mark the damaged area on the object). Arrayed outside the circle are the corresponding Latin and modern-day Hebrew letters. According to the late Nahman Avigad, widely considered the most eminent Hebrew epigraphist of his time, the inscription reads, "qdš khnm lb[yt yhw]h"—"Holy to the priests, belonging to the h[ouse of Yahweh]h." The letters in brackets have been restored. A few scholars argue that the damaged portion of the inscription can just as easily be restored to read, "belonging to the h[ouse of Ashera]h," a reference to the Canaanite fertility goddess. Avigad has countered, however, that the phrase "temple of Yahweh" appears hundreds of times in the Bible, but despite Asherah's popularity at the time, not once do we have the expression "temple of Asherah." Avigad added that if the goddess were the subject of the inscription, it would have to read "the Asherah," and there is no room for the required additional letter.

Three paleographers (experts in dating inscriptions based on the shape and stance of letters)—Avigad, Frank Moore Cross of Harvard and the French scholar André Lemaire—have dated the inscription to the second half of the eighth century B.C.E. More specifically, the ivory pomegranate might well date to the reign of King Hezekiah (727 to 698 B.C.E.), who ordered a religious reform that attempted to centralize all Israelite worship in the Jerusalem Temple. All three scholars also agree on the restoration of the missing letters.

sing letters be restored?

In the following drawing by the late Professor Nahman Avigad of Hebrew University, the solid letters have been copied from the shoulder of the pomegranate; the letters in outline have been restored. Note that three letters have survived in part. Three are wholly missing:

Now let us look at this in modern Hebrew letters, in transcription, in transliteration and in translation. In each case the letters in brackets have been wholly or partially restored.

קדש כהנם לב[ית יהו]ה

qdš khnm lb[yt yhw]h

"Qodeš kohanim, l-b[eyt Yahwe]h."

"Holy to the priests, belonging to the H[ouse of Yahwe]h."

The first word, *qodeš* (or more recognizable to an American eye, *kodesh*) means holiness. Professor Avigad would translate the first phrase "Sacred donation for the priests," suggesting that the scepter was a gift to the priests of the temple to be used in the temple service.

The more difficult question arises in connection with the restoration in the second phrase. The first letter, l (or *lamed*), preceding a noun regularly means "belonging to." About this, there is agreement. The next letter is clearly b (or *beth*). Everyone agrees that this word must be completed to read "belonging to the house (or temple) of ...," especially because the last two letters have been partially preserved. There is no other sensible way to restore this word. House, incidentally, designates a temple as well as a domestic structure. A temple was the house of the deity.

Whose temple was it—the Israelite God Yahweh* or some other deity? The last letter has partially survived, so we know that it is an h (or *heb*). The obvious restoration, but not the only possible one, is Yahweh. And this tells us that the inscribed ivory pomegranate was used in Solomon's Temple, the temple dedicated to Yahweh.

One more element is critical—the date of the pomegranate. This takes us to the science—or art—of paleography.

Paleography is the study of scripts. The date of an inscription like that on the shoulder of the pomegranate can be determined by the shape of the letters, their form and their stance.

When the Jews returned from the Babylonian Exile, they brought with them the Aramaic script, a direct descendant of which is the Jewish script that is still used to write Hebrew today. Before the Babylonian destruction of the Solomonic Temple in 586 B.C.E., however, Hebrew was written in what scholars call paleo-Hebrew script. It is rather easy to tell that this inscription was carved in the ivory before 586 B.C.E. Moreover, after that date there would have been no Temple until it was rebuilt later in the sixth century B.C.E.

But because paleo-Hebrew script changed over time, paleographers can provide more specific dates for inscriptions. A mark of the sophistication that paleography has reached is reflected in the narrow range of dates offered by various experts. The inscription on this pomegranate has been paleographically dated by three of the world's most prominent experts—Frank Moore Cross of Harvard, the late Nahman Avigad of Hebrew University and André Lemaire of the Centre National de la Recherche Scientifique in Paris. Lemaire dates the inscription to the late-eighth century B.C.E. Avigad and Cross date it to the mid-eighth century. Not much difference—somewhere between, say, 765 and 705 B.C.E.

King Solomon reigned from about 960 B.C.E. to 920 B.C.E. According to the

*In Hebrew, the name consists of the four letters YHWH, *yod, heh, waw, heh,* known as the Tetragrammaton. In many English translations of the Bible, YHWH is translated LORD. (*Elohim,* by contrast, is translated as the generic name God). YHWH is the unpronounceable personal name of Israel's God. No one is sure how these four Hebrew letters were pronounced by the high priest once a year in the Holy of Holies in the Temple, but by scholarly convention, the name is pronounced Yahweh.

✝ ᴡ ◀ ۹ ᖾ ٦ □ ₣ ٦ ᕰ ᒪ ۶ ؟ ⦵ ᖾ ٤ Ψ ∃ ٩ ٦ ◁ ✳

א ב ג ד ה ו ז ח ט י כ ל מ נ ס ע פ פ צ ק ר ש ת

T S R Q TS P ' S N M L K Y T KH Z W H D G B '
SH   F   V   V

*Ancient Hebrew script, called paleo-Hebrew, is
shown in the chart, together with modern Hebrew
forms and counterparts in the Latin alphabet.
Paleo-Hebrew ceased to be commonly used after the
Babylonian destruction of Jerusalem and the
Temple in 586 B.C.E. Paleographers, experts in the
evolution of scripts, have further narrowed the date
of the inscription on the pomegranate in this exhibit
to the eighth century B.C.E., the same period as the
examples on the chart.*

Bible, he began to construct the Temple in the fourth year of his reign (1 Kings 6:1,37;
2 Chronicles 3:2) and completed it in his eleventh year, having taken seven years to
build it (1 Kings 6:38). For the task, he mustered 70,000 basket carriers, 80,000 quar-
riers and 3,300 supervisors (3,600 in Chronicles) (1 Kings 5:29-30; 2 Chronicles 2:1).

Clearly our pomegranate does not come from Solomon's reign. But it does come
from his Temple, which lasted until the Babylonians destroyed it in 586 B.C.E. It may
well date to the reign of King Hezekiah who ruled Judah from about 727 to 698 B.C.E.
Hezekiah led a religious reform that tried to make the Jerusalem Temple the center of
all Israelite worship.

In our consideration of the date of the pomegranate, we have omitted the first
and clearly the most important factor archaeologists normally look at: where the object
was found. The reason we have omitted this factor is simple—we don't know!

This brings us to one of the most fascinating (and mysterious) aspects of the
pomegranate—how it came to light and was finally acquired by the Israel Museum
(after first being smuggled out of Israel).

HOW THE IVORY POMEGRANATE CAME TO LIGHT

PARISIAN SCHOLAR ANDRÉ LEMAIRE, WHOM WE HAVE ALREADY MET, SPENT THE SUMMER OF
1979 at the Ecole Biblique in Jerusalem, studying, as usual, ancient Semitic inscriptions.
One hot day in July, Lemaire wandered into the shop of an antiquities dealer, looking
for anything with an inscription on it. The antiquities dealer knew Lemaire from previous visits and told him that he had recently seen a small inscribed object; he could
get it for Lemaire to see, if he liked. Lemaire said he would indeed like to see it. On
the appointed day, Lemaire returned to the shop. The antiquities dealer greeted the
slender middle-aged scholar. They drank tea, and the dealer proceeded to show the
scholar our tiny pomegranate. Lemaire was permitted to photograph the object and proceeded to publish the inscription, with a description and analysis in French, in an

obscure scholarly journal, the *Revue Biblique*, published by the Dominican fathers of the Ecole Biblique. Oddly enough, Lemaire's three-page article hardly caused a ripple. No one talked about it and no one was concerned about it.

To find articles for *Biblical Archaeology Review (BAR)*, we regularly comb the scholarly journals and in this process discovered Lemaire's French article. We contacted him and persuaded him to write an article on the pomegranate and its inscription for *BAR*. The picture of the pomegranate Lemaire had published was in black-and-white; we wanted color pictures for *BAR*. Lemaire returned to the antiquities dealer and was able to arrange for color pictures of the pomegranate. This was not simply a gratuitous gesture on the part of the owner. Publication of a color picture of the pomegranate in *BAR* would vastly increase the value of the object. Scholars often face this problem: When presented with an unprovenanced artifact that might be the product of an illicit excavation, should the scholar study it and publish it, thereby making it available to the world but thereby also providing the owner a pedigree for what may be contraband?

In January 1984, Lemaire's article appeared in *BAR*, giving the pomegranate instant worldwide attention and recognition.

Despite this publicity, all efforts to find the owner—or even to identify the antiquities dealer—failed. *BAR* published a plea for the owner to identify himself or herself—"or at least to allow the Israel Museum to display the inscribed ivory pomegranate anonymously."[1] The magazine called on the Israeli Attorney General and the Israeli Department of Antiquities to investigate—all to no avail.

Then in December 1987 a tour guide named Meir Urbach walked into the office of Meir Mayer, the Israel Museum's public relations director, and threw on his desk a copy of *Biblical Archaeology Review* opened to Lemaire's article. Urbach asked Mayer if the museum would be interested in purchasing the pomegranate. The price: $600,000!

Meir Urbach is no ordinary tour guide. He is the son of the late Ephraim Urbach, one of Israel's greatest talmudic scholars. Urbach has studied Talmud and archaeology at Hebrew University. He has acted as a guide for 18 years, primarily for prominent visitors. Urbach still claims not to know who "owned" the pomegranate, however; he says he was approached through intermediaries. And, he says, he is not permitted to talk. He does say, however, that he was not told to whom he should offer the pomegranate. Offering it to the Israel Museum was his idea; that is where it should be displayed, he says. The person with whom he dealt—"who represented someone who represented someone else who represented the owner"—was surprised that he offered it to the museum ("He didn't think I would be such an idiot"), but all the seller wanted was the money—$600,000.

The acquisitions committee of the museum promptly approved the purchase, hoping to negotiate for a lower price. Then began a campaign to raise the money. The museum's fund-raising effort proved dismally unsuccessful. For four months, museum fund-raisers pounded on doors, but came away empty-handed.

In the meantime, the pomegranate appeared in an important exhibit at the Grand Palais in Paris in 1988. Somehow it had been smuggled out of Israel. Then one day in April 1988, out of the blue, an agent advised the Israel Museum that it would receive an unrestricted gift of one million Swiss francs, approximately $675,000, from a donor in Basel.

The museum often receives anonymous gifts, sometimes large ones like this. But museum officials always know the donor. This was the first time the museum received a gift anywhere near this size when no one at the museum knew who the donor was.

Through the donor's agent, the museum asked the donor if it would be appropriate to use the bulk of the money to purchase the pomegranate. Word came back that the donor approved. Negotiations for the purchase of the pomegranate were then completed and a final price of $550,000 was agreed upon.

Is there any connection between the anonymous donor and the then-owner of the pomegranate? Or was it just a coincidence that a gift sufficient to purchase the pomegranate arrived just when it was needed? One rumor has it that when the museum could not raise the money, the owner of the pomegranate began to feel guilty about depriving Israel of its cultural patrimony—not to mention breaking its laws—and decided to save face by providing the museum with the money to "buy" the pomegranate.

In late spring of 1988, the museum was told it could pick up the pomegranate in Zurich. Payment was to be made by a deposit in a numbered account in Zurich. The museum drew the funds to pay for the pomegranate from a deposit made by the anonymous donor and drawn on a numbered Swiss account.

When Itzchaq Tzur, the museum's then-deputy director for administration, flew to Zurich for the exchange, he also took Professor Avigad to make sure the pomegranate was authentic. When the two men entered the appointed meeting place in Zurich, they were handed a bag marked "Happy Birthday" by a man named David Jesselson, a former Israeli who lives in Zurich, an economist whose hobby is archaeology. Inside the bag was the pomegranate, which Avigad proceeded to examine meticulously. When he pronounced it sound, the payment money was released and Avigad and Tzur left for Israel with their precious "Happy Birthday" bag.

Thus the pomegranate came to the Israel Museum, where it has been displayed until its trip to the United States for this exhibit.

According to our sources, the pomegranate, for which the Israel Museum paid $550,000, was originally purchased from the antiquities dealer for $3,000. Today, however, even $550,000 seems like a bargain. In Frank Cross's words, "The pomegranate is priceless."

Yet there are still some doubts.

THE DOUBTERS

AT FIRST, SOME QUESTIONED THE POMEGRANATE'S AUTHENTICITY. IT COULD BE A FAKE, THEY said. But this is rarely heard today. It has passed the scrupulous standards of three world-renowned experts. In addition, in his initial examination of the pomegranate, Lemaire put it under a microscope and noticed traces of new incisions at the bottom of some letters, as if someone had tried to clean out caked earth from the incised letters with a small needle. But whoever cleaned the letters left some of the ancient patina in the incisions. This, together with the shapes of the letters, resolved the question of authenticity.

A few scholars have also questioned the reconstruction of the name of the deity in the inscription. It may not be Yahweh, they say. There are other ancient deities whose name ends in a *heh*. The most vocal doubter is Aharon Kempinski, an archaeologist at Tel Aviv University. According to Kempinski, the missing letters in the name of the deity could as easily be restored to read "[Ashera]h," the Canaanite fertility goddess, as [Yahwe]h, the personal name of the Israelite God.[2] Another possibility that has been suggested is [Ba'ala]h, the feminine form of the Canaanite god Ba'al. In Hebrew each of these deities is spelled with four letters, the last of which is a *heh*: YHWH, 'SRH and B'LH.

Avigad and others strongly disagree with Kempinski.[3] Avigad points out that the phrase *beyt Yahweh* or "temple of Yahweh" appears hundreds of times in the Bible. It also appears on an ostracon (a pottery sherd with writing) excavated at a temple of Yahweh in Arad, in the Negev.[4] By contrast, Asherah, the consort of Ba'al, is mentioned approximately 40 times in the Bible, but not once do we find any reference to a "temple of Asherah."

Despite the popularity of Asherah in Judah and Israel, she apparently did not have a temple of her own, Avigad argues. Avigad also rejects Kempinski's suggestion on grammatical grounds: If the goddess were meant, it would have to be "temple of *the* asherah" (*heh* in Hebrew). There is no room for an additional letter in the space available, says Avigad.

"Even if the [inscribed ivory] pomegranate could be shown with certainty to have originated in Solomon's Temple," Kempinski argues, "the price paid [$550,000] is far above its value." The Israel Museum purchased it "in no small measure because of Hershel Shanks' claim that it was a holy object that should be redeemed."

Unfortunately, we will never know where this pomegranate was discovered—or how. There are several possibilities. Perhaps the most likely is that a workman in a Jerusalem excavation discovered the pomegranate and simply pocketed it, later selling it to an antiquities dealer. Another possibility is that it was discovered in an illicit excavation. A third possibility is that it turned up by accident, as not infrequently happens in Israel, perhaps even in a dump from a Jerusalem excavation.

In any event, it is now owned by the Israel Museum and is permanently displayed in Jerusalem. We are grateful that the museum has graciously allowed it to come to the United States for this short visit.

ENDNOTES

[1] "Plea for Owner of Solomon's Temple Relic to Identify Himself," *Biblical Archaeology Review* May/June 1984, p. 6.

[2] Aharon Kempinski, "Is It Really a Pomegranate from the 'Temple of Yahweh?'" *Qadmoniot* 23 (1990), p. 126 [in Hebrew].

[3] Nahman Avigad, "It Is Indeed a Pomegranate from the 'Temple of Yahweh,'" *Qadmoniot* 24 (1991), p. 60 [in Hebrew].

[4] See Ze'ev Herzog, Miriam Aharoni and Anson F. Rainey, "Arad—An Ancient Israelite Fortress with a Temple to Yahweh," *Biblical Archaeology Review*, March/April 1987, p. 35; and Yohanan Aharoni, *Arad Inscriptions* (Jerusalem: Israel Exploration Society, 1981), inscription 18, pp. 35-38.

BIBLIOGRAPHY

Artzy, Michal, "Pomegranate Scepters and Incense Stand with Pomegranates Found in Priest's Grave," *Biblical Archaeology Review*, January/February 1990, pp. 48-51.

Avigad, Nahman, "The Inscribed Pomegranate from the 'House of the Lord,' " *The Israel Museum Journal* 8 (1989), pp. 7-16.

Avigad, Nahman, "It Is Indeed a Pomegranate from the 'House of the Lord,' " *Qadmoniot* 24 (1991) [in Hebrew], pp. 60-61.

Kempinski, Aharon, "Is It Really a Pomegranate from the 'House of the Lord?' " *Qadmoniot* 23 (1990) [in Hebrew], p. 126.

Lemaire, André, "Une inscription paleo-hebraique sur grenade en ivoire," *Revue Biblique* 88 (1981), pp. 236-239.

Lemaire, André, "Probable Head of Priestly Scepter from Solomon's Temple Surfaces in Jerusalem," *Biblical Archaeology Review*, January/February 1984, pp. 24-29.

Muthmann, F., *Der Granatapfel, Symbol des Lebens in der alten Welt* (Bern, 1982).

Shanks, Hershel, "The Pomegranate Scepter Head—From the Temple of the Lord or from a Temple of Asherah?" *Biblical Archaeology Review*, May/June 1992, pp. 42-45.

Shanks, Hershel, "Pomegranate: Sole Relic From Solomon's Temple, Smuggled Out of Israel, Now Recovered," *Moment*, December 1988, pp. 36-43.

Shanks, Hershel, "Was BAR an Accessory to Highway Robbery?" *Biblical Archaeology Review*, November/December 1988, p. 66.

THE OSSUARY
OF THE
HIGH PRIEST
CAIAPHAS

FOR ABOUT A HUNDRED YEARS AT THE TURN OF THE ERA, CHIEFLY IN JERUSALEM, an unusual burial custom developed—the reburial of the bones of the deceased in smallish, rectangular bone boxes called ossuaries. During the period of the Israelite monarchy, from the tenth through the sixth centuries B.C.E., special concern was also expressed for the bones of the deceased. But they were not reburied in ossuaries. At that time in Jerusalem, it was customary to lay the deceased on a rock-cut burial bench in a burial cave; after about a year, when the flesh had decayed, the bones were deposited with the bones from previous burials in a repository under the stone burial bench. Some scholars have speculated that this is what is meant by the Biblical phrase to be "gathered to their fathers" (Judges 2:10; 2 Kings 22:20) or "buried with his fathers" (2 Kings 8:24) or "slept with his fathers" (2 Kings 13:13). But no ossuaries were used to house bones in the period of the Israelite monarchy.

Ossuaries were used, however, in the late Second Temple period, which ended with the Roman destruction of the Temple in 70 C.E. A few examples can be found for a hundred years or so thereafter.

The standard Jewish cave-tomb in Jerusalem during the time ossuaries were used included a forecourt through which the cave-tomb was entered. The cave was generally carved in soft limestone. On entering, one stepped down into a rectangular standing pit that was created by the carving of stone benches on the sides. The standing pit allowed ancient mourners and workmen to stand erect and operate in the low-ceilinged cave. Into the walls were carved deep cavities called loculi (kokhim in Hebrew). Each loculus (koch) was about 6 feet deep and 1.5 feet wide and high, often with a slightly arched top at the opening.

The bodies were initially buried in the loculi. After about a year, when the flesh had decayed, the bones were reburied in rectangular ossuaries that were then placed in the loculi or upon the rock-cut benches. Frequently, more than one ossuary was placed in a single loculus, and often the bones of more than one person were placed in a single ossuary.

While constructing a water park in Jerusalem's Peace Forest, workmen stumbled upon an ancient burial cave with a dozen ossuaries, or bone boxes. Shown opposite is the most elaborate. Its exquisitely decorated facade features two large circles, each composed of five rosettes surrounding a center rosette; stylized branches frame the sides and top. The ossuary measures about 2.5 feet long, 1 foot wide and 1.25 feet high. On the back and on one side are inscriptions—with a slight variation in spelling— reading "Yehosef bar Qafa'" (Joseph son of Caiaphas). Excavators discovered the bones of six different people inside this ossuary: four young people, an adult woman and a man about 60 years old. The remains of the man may be those of the high priest described in the New Testament as having interrogated Jesus before delivering him to the Roman authorities.

Thousands of ossuaries from the late Second Temple period have been discovered in and around Jerusalem. Two large whorl rosettes decorate the front face of an ossuary (lower right), one of several on display at the Israel Museum. The photo mural depicts a burial chamber in the so-called Tomb of the Sanhedrin, an elaborate burial cave complex located on a hill in northern Jerusalem. These ossuaries display three types of lids: flat, gabled (triangular) and vaulted (curved). Ossuaries were usually made from a single block of limestone; they average 2 feet in length, 1 foot in width and a little more than 1 foot in height.

The ossuaries were usually made from a single block of limestone, rarely of clay. They are about 2 feet long, 1 foot wide and 1 foot high (usually a little higher than wide). Children's ossuaries are smaller. Many ossuaries have four tiny feet. The ossuary lids may be flat, gabled (triangular) or curved (vaulted).

The ossuaries are often decorated, mostly with geometric designs, but sometimes with architectural and plant motifs. No human figures or faces appear on the ossuaries, however; they were made by an observant Jewish community that strictly interpreted the Second Commandment forbidding graven images (Exodus 20:4 / Deuteronomy 5:8).

A number of the ossuaries also have inscriptions. Usually these are graffiti-like inscriptions to commemorate and preserve the name of the deceased, occasionally mentioning the age, profession, or place of origin, or stating that the deceased was a proselyte. Ossuary inscriptions are found in Greek, Aramaic and Hebrew, and sometimes in more than one language on the same ossuary.

The ideology of secondary burial, or ossilegium, to use the technical term, is unclear. According to some scholars, ossuary burials in this period reflect a belief in individual physical resurrection of the body, for which purpose the bones were collected and preserved. A leading scholar on the subject, L. Y. Rahmani, tells us that the year-long process of decomposition of the flesh was thought to be a painful atonement for sins, after which the sinless bones were ready for resurrection. The Talmud rules that an executed criminal could not be buried with his father until the flesh had wasted away, presumably to atone for the crime, leaving the bones in an appropriately sinless condition.[1]

The ossuary in this exhibit is of special interest for two reasons: It is especially beautiful, and it probably contained the bones of the high priest Caiaphas, who, according to the Gospels, presided at the trial of Jesus.

THE DISCOVERY OF THE OSSUARY

CORPSES WERE CONSIDERED TO POSSESS THE UTMOST DEGREE OF CULTIC IMPURITY. HENCE they were always buried outside the city boundaries. Ancient tombs surround ancient Jerusalem—on the north, south, east and west. More than 800 tombs from the Second Temple period alone have been discovered in Jerusalem. So it was hardly surprising when the Israel Antiquities Authority received a call one cold morning in November 1990 notifying the Authority that bulldozers in the Peace Forest south of Jerusalem, moving dirt to create a children's water park, had hit an ancient tomb.

The Antiquities Authority immediately dispatched archaeologist Zvi Greenhut to the site. When he got there, Greenhut found that the roof of the cave had already collapsed. Without even excavating he could peer inside, into the tomb's central chamber, where he saw ossuaries strewn about (see p. 38). Once inside, Greenhut observed four loculi carved into the rock walls (see plan, p. 40). Additional ossuaries were in the loculi.

An immediate rescue excavation was undertaken. The excavators were able to reconstruct the original floor plan of the cave-tomb—a forecourt, a narrow entrance that had been closed with a blocking stone (see p. 38), a standing pit, another pit that may have been used as a repository for bones that were not placed in ossuaries and four loculi. The cave was apparently the burial site of a small family (only four loculi had been cut into the walls—three in one wall and one in another), but the large number of ossuaries (12) and the bones of so many individuals (63) indicate that this tomb was probably used for several generations.

Several of the ossuaries were decorated and had inscriptions. Two of them were scratched with a form of the name Caiaphas (see p. 42-43)—Qafa' and Qayafa'—which suggests that this was the burial cave of the Caiaphas clan or family.

The name Caiaphas is well known from the New Testament and from the work of the first-century C.E. Jewish historian Flavius Josephus. Later, in rabbinic literature, the

An elegant attic-style doorway leads to a tomb complex south of Jerusalem's Temple Mount. Architectural fragments found scattered around the Temple Mount resemble the style of this doorway, leading scholars to believe that the tomb complex held the remains of a priestly family that served in the Temple. (Incidentally, the Temple could be seen from this tomb.) If the scholars are correct, the entrance to the Caiaphas family tomb may originally have looked something like this doorway.

Summoned to the burial cave by workmen, archaeologists found six ossuaries scattered about the central burial chamber. Four others had been moved by the workers, and two ossuaries remained undisturbed in loculus IV.

Visitors to the tomb would have had to crawl through the narrow entrance, shown here from the inside. The entryway's blocking stone stands at left. Just inside the entrance lies a rectangular pit, that allowed mourners to stand inside the chamber.

name again appears in various forms. The Tosefta speaks of the House of Qefai, or Caiaphas.[2]

The tomb was found just where we might expect to find the cave-tomb of a priestly family; it lies near a well-known group of highly decorated cave-tombs of prominent families dating to this same period. This kind of burial was not for everyone. It was reserved for the Temple aristocracy, landed gentry and wealthy merchants. The simple earth burials of the poor have long since vanished.

CAIAPHAS IN THE NEW TESTAMENT

CAIAPHAS IS REFERRED TO IN THREE OF THE FOUR GOSPELS (MATTHEW, LUKE AND JOHN) and in Acts. These texts identify "Caiaphas" as the high priest who presided at the trial of Jesus. The accounts conflict, and most scholars question their accuracy in various details. But the name Caiaphas is an authentic one. Josephus identifies a man named "Joseph who was called Caiaphas" who served as high priest between 18 and 36 C.E. This Caiaphas achieved the high-priesthood by marrying the daughter of Annas, who had served as high priest before him. Although this detail is reported only in John 18:13, it too is generally accepted as accurate. (Incidentally, an ossuary of a member of the Annas family has also been recovered.) Annas was appointed to the priestly office by the Roman prefect Quirinius in 6 C.E. Another Roman prefect, Valerius Gratus, deposed Annas in 15 C.E., a reflection of Roman power in the choice of the Jewish high priest. Annas's son Jonathan succeeded Caiaphas as high priest in 36 C.E. after a Roman governor of Syria, L. Vitellius, deposed Caiaphas. (Acts 4:6 links Annas, Caiaphas and a certain John, whom scholars believe to be Jonathan, a conclusion also supported by some ancient texts of Acts.)

The Annas clan belonged to the Sadducees, as opposed to the Pharisees. We know this not only from Josephus, but also from Acts 5:17, which refers to "the high priest...and all who were with him, that is, the party of the Sadducees." Appointed by the Romans, these Sadducean high priests were known as harsh judges. According to Josephus, they "are indeed more heartless than any of the other Jews...when they sit in judgment" (*Antiquities of the Jews* 20.199).

It was the high priest identified as Caiaphas in three of the Gospels who asked Jesus the decisive question, "Are you the Messiah?" (Matthew 26:62-63; Mark 14:60-62). The synoptic Gospels (Matthew, Mark and Luke) do not indicate precisely why the priestly circles sought to silence Jesus, although it is clear that he represented a threat to their authority. Moreover, he was popular with the people—"all the people hung on his words" (Luke 19:48). According to the Gospel of John, Jesus' enemies feared that the Romans would destroy them because of Jesus' preaching (John 11:48). New Testament scholar David Flusser of Hebrew University in Jerusalem tells us that Caiaphas probably decided to act because he feared that the Jesus movement and its possible success among the Jews would cause violent Roman intervention. Caiaphas's anxiety was perhaps exaggerated but not unfounded. Roman military forces not only fought against Jewish rebels, but also crushed any enthusiastic Jewish prophetic movement that aimed to free Israel. Theudas, mentioned in Acts 5:36, led one such movement. Josephus described his career:

> "Theudas persuaded the majority of the masses to take up their possessions and to follow him to the Jordan River. He stated that he was a prophet and that at his command the river would be parted and would provide them an easy passage. With this talk he deceived many. Fadus, however, did not permit them to reap the fruit of their folly, but sent against them a squadron of cavalry. These fell upon them unexpectedly, slew many of them and took many prisoners. Theudas himself was captured, whereupon they cut off his head and brought it to Jerusalem." (*Antiquities of the Jews* 20.97-98).

In a second case reported by Josephus, another group of Jews went into the desert in the belief that God would there show them tokens of deliverance. Felix, the Roman governor of Judea, "regarding this as but the preliminary to insurrection, sent a body of cavalry and heavy-armed infantry, and put a large number to the sword" (Josephus, *The Jewish War* 2.258-260).

The arched tops of loculus I (right) and II can be seen in this view. They are located in the tomb's west wall, opposite the entrance.

Undisturbed for two thousand years, a pair of ossuaries lie inside loculus IV. The one on the left is the beautifully decorated ossuary of Caiaphas, the high priest at the time of Jesus.

PLAN

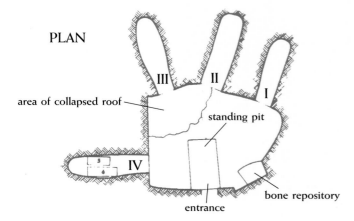

area of collapsed roof

III   II   I

standing pit

IV

bone repository

entrance

SECTION

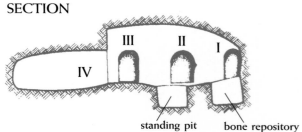

III   II   I

IV

standing pit   bone repository

An overview of the Caiaphas tomb. The plan at top shows the burial cave as seen from above, while the cross-section shows the view as if the tomb were sliced vertically. A narrow entranceway leads into the tomb chamber; a rectangular pit, dug below floor level, allowed workers or mourners to stand upright. Four 6-foot-deep by 1.5-foot-wide cavities were carved into the chamber's soft limestone walls. Known as loculi (singular loculus; kokh and kokhim in Hebrew), these niches were used for initial burial and later to house ossuaries. Ossuary 6 in loculus IV was the elaborate Caiaphas ossuary. To the right of the entrance is a pit that served as repository for bones that were not placed in ossuaries.

Caiaphas could reasonably have feared that Jesus' activity would lead to a similar end and even to the catastrophic destruction of the Temple.

Caiaphas justified his fateful decision by arguing for its expediency: Let one man die and not the whole nation (John 11:50). In the words of David Flusser:

"Many a politician and ruler before and after Caiaphas has believed that real or assumed expediency outweighs any moral scruple. This argumentation and behavior was (and is) without doubt contrary to the Jewish faith's basic humane approach[3]—but a Sadducean high priest could disagree."[4]

The Pharisees, had they been in power, would probably have acted differently. We have already seen that Josephus regarded the Sadducees as heartless judges. When Jesus' apostles were arrested after the crucifixion, their lives were saved by a "Pharisee called Gamaliel, a teacher of the law held in high regard by all the people" (Acts 5:34). This Gamaliel was Rabban Gamaliel the Elder, a major Pharisaic leader. The Pharisees, it seems, disagreed with the judgment of the Sadducees regarding Jesus. Moreover, according to Pharisaic *halakhah* (religious law), the handing over of a Jew to a foreign authority was forbidden; to do so was an unforgivable sin.[5] Recurring once again to the words of David Flusser, for the Pharisees, "the whole affair [involving the apostles] was further proof of Sadducean cruelty." By contrast, "A critical reading of the Gospels demonstrates that the Pharisees did not play a decisive role in Jesus' passion and crucifixion."[6] This has been observed by many scholars.[7] Indeed, the Pharisees are not mentioned by name in the Synoptic Gospels' description of Jesus' trial and condemnation.

That matters might have been different had the Pharisees been in power is further supported by another episode that occurred after Jesus' crucifixion. A subsequent Sadducean high priest had Jesus' brother James condemned. "The most fair-minded [people who were also] strict in the observance of the commandments"—that is, the Pharisees—engineered the deposition of the high priest as a result of the illegal condemnation of James (*Antiquities of the Jews* 20.200-203).

"Joseph son of Caiaphas" reads the graffiti-like inscriptions on the elaborately carved ossuary. The single-line inscription, at left, appears on the ossuary's narrow side. The two-line inscription was incised on the back of the ossuary and contains a slight variation in spelling: The name Qafa' contains an additional letter; in this inscription, it is spelled with a yod. (Also see the drawings on page 42 and 43.)

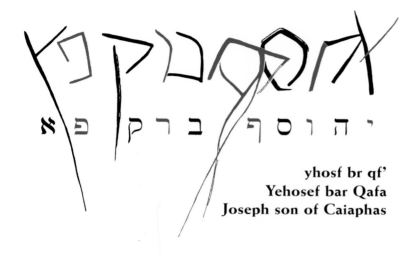

yhosf br qf'
Yehosef bar Qafa
Joseph son of Caiaphas

The drawings of these two inscriptions (above and opposite page) are painted in alternating colors to help distinguish each letter from those adjoining. Below the inscriptions, in the same colors, are the individual letters in their modern Hebrew equivalents. In addition, a transcription in Latin letters, a transliteration and a translation are also provided. Though the New Testament calls the high priest who tried Jesus by the single name of Caiaphas, the first-century C.E.

Jewish historian Josephus refers to a "Joseph who was called Caiaphas of the high priesthood" who held the office at this time. Caiaphas is therefore believed to be a family nickname that was passed on from generation to generation. The name may derive from a word meaning "basket" or "carrying" or "wooden rod" as used in roofing or for the support of vines. The family patriarch who first introduced the name may have been a basketmaker, or one who used pack-animals to move goods or worked in the vineyard business.

THE OSSUARY INSCRIPTIONS

BOTH THE NEW TESTAMENT AND JOSEPHUS RECORD THE NAME CAIAPHAS IN GREEK. ON the two ossuaries bearing the name we have for the first time the original Semitic form of the name in a contemporary inscription, that is, in Aramaic, a language closely related to Hebrew that was the vernacular of the time.

One of the two ossuaries with this name scratched into it is inscribed with nothing more than the four Semitic letters that spell "Qafa'." The other ossuary, the one in this exhibit, is even more interesting. It is twice incised with the name "Joseph son of Caiaphas." It is this ossuary that may well have contained the bones of the high priest.

The ossuary is fit for a high priest. It is unusually beautiful and highly decorated—clearly the most elaborate of the 12 found in the tomb. It is also the largest—2 feet, 5 inches long; 11.5 inches wide; and 1 foot, 3 inches high. By contrast the smallest ossuary found in this tomb is only 1 foot, 6.5 inches long. The lid of the largest ossuary is curved and only slightly decorated with double dotted lines forming a series of rectangles on the edge. Only one side (one of the long sides) of the ossuary is decorated. It is, however, the facade, the only side meant to be exposed.

The ossuary is a masterpiece of the stone carver's art. It is decorated in a rare and intricate pattern of two circles, each containing six whorl rosettes—one in the middle with five encircling it. Stylized branches frame the two large circles, running up each side of the ossuary and along the top, culminating in a small six-petalled rosette. Four small palmettes fill the corners inside the frame around the large rosettes. The style reflects a *horror vacui;* ornamentation fills all available space.

The ossuary was originally painted, and some of the paint has survived. Every other petal of three small six-petalled rosettes on the ossuary—one at top center and one at the top of each of the two larger groups of rosettes—was painted orange, as we can tell from the paint that still remains. Traces of orange paint can also be seen on the lid and elsewhere on the ossuary.

In contrast to the highly skilled artistry decorating the front of the ossuary, the two inscriptions are scratched roughly, one on the side and the other on the back of the ossuary. Among the finds in the excavation of the tomb were two iron nails. Apparently these were used to scratch the inscriptions after the bones had been collected and placed in the ossuaries and perhaps even after the ossuaries had been placed in their loculi.

The inscription on the side of the ossuary is in one line; the one on the back is in two. Otherwise, the two inscriptions are identical, except for a slight difference in the spelling of Caiaphas. On the back, Caiaphas is spelled with an additional letter, a *yod* (y), that may have functioned as a vowel (a *mater lectionis*) in a writing system that is essentially consonantal. (Incidentally, Josephus's Greek references to Caiaphas reflect the same variation in spelling.) To the right and on the opposite page are the two inscriptions—first a drawing, then a transcription in Hebrew letters. Below them we have printed a transcription in Latin letters, a transliteration and a translation. To help you distinguish the letters of the roughly scratched graffiti, we have printed every other letter in a different color, both in the drawing and in the Hebrew transcription.

The letters are in cursive Jewish script typical of ossuary inscriptions of this period. The inscription on the back is written from bottom to top, an indication that it was probably scratched in the ossuary after it had been placed in the loculus. While the inscription on the side is written properly from right to left, it too was probably incised after the ossuary was placed in the loculus. Clearly, these inscriptions were not meant for public display.

Some of the letters in this cursive script will look strange even to readers of modern Hebrew. For example, the *aleph* is missing its left leg, as is the case in many other ossuary inscriptions.

According to Dr. Ronny Reich of the Israel Antiquities Authority, who has written the definitive analysis of these inscriptions, the name Caiaphas probably func-

יהוסף בר

yhosf br
Yehosef bar
Joseph son of

קיפא

qyf'
Qayafa
Caiaphas

tioned as a kind of family nickname, passed on from generation to generation. A recent statistical study of the onomasticon of this period indicates that only four names account for 28 percent of all the men's names. One of these was Joseph. "In these circumstances," Reich tells us, "a family nickname may well have been a good means of distinguishing among people with the same personal name."[8]

Josephus indicates that this was the case with Caiaphas. He speaks of the high priest as "Joseph who is called Caiaphas." We have translated the inscriptions on this ossuary literally as "Joseph son of Caiaphas," but this does not mean that Joseph was biologically the son of Caiaphas. "Son of..." is used in the sense of belonging to the same group or family, as when a student at Yale is referred to as a "son of Eli." More properly translated, our inscription should read, "Joseph of the family of Caiaphas." Since there were no last names then as we know them today, we should understand the name Caiaphas as a kind of family or clan nickname.

The meaning of this name is a puzzle. The best scholarly guess is that it is etymologically related to something like "basket" or "carrying" or perhaps a "wooden rod" used either for roofing or for the support of vines. This might mean that the forefather of the family, who introduced the nickname, was a basketmaker, or used pack asses to move goods, or was active in the vineyard business, building supports for vines.

The ossuary contained bones from six different people: two infants, a child between two and five, a young boy between 13 and 18, an adult woman—and a male of about 60 years! This might well be the bones of the high priest who presided at the trial of Jesus. The only other thing we know about him from his bones, if the foot bones in the ossuary are his, is that he had a severe degenerative joint disease. After study by paleo-osteologist Joseph Zias of the Antiquities Authority, the bones were delivered, as is customary, to the Ministry of Religious Affairs, and were then reburied on the Mount of Olives.

ENDNOTES

[1] L.Y. Rahmani, "Ancient Jerusalem's Funerary Customs and Tombs—Part One," *Biblical Archaeologist* 44/3 (1981), p. 175.

[2] Tosefta, *Yevamot* 1:10.

[3] See Tosefta, *Terumot* 7:20. In such cases the Hasidic *halakhah* did not permit any compromise. See W. Bacher, *Die Agada der Palästinensischen Amoraer*, (Hildesheim, Germany: I. Strassburg, Repr. G. Olms, 1892 [1965]), pp. 128, 188-189.

[4] David Flusser, "Caiaphas in the New Testament," *'Atiqot (English Series)* 21 (1992), p. 85.

[5] Seder Olam Rabba, ch. 3, verse 11.

[6] Flusser, pp. 84-85.

[7] See, e.g., P. Winter, *On the Trial of Jesus* (Berlin, 1961), pp. 125-126; A.F.J. Klijn, "Scribes, Pharisees, High-Priests and Elders," *Novum Testamentum* 3 (1959), pp. 254-267.

[8] Ronny Reich, "Caiaphas Name Inscribed on Bone Boxes," *Biblical Archaeology Review*, Sept./Oct. 1992, p. 41.

BIBLIOGRAPHY

Flusser, David, "Caiaphas in the New Testament," *'Atiqot* (English Series) 21 (1992), pp. 81-87.

Geva, Hillel, and Ronny Reich, "Burial Caves on Mount Scopus," *'Atiqot* (Hebrew Series) 8 (1982), pp. 52-56.

Greenhut, Zvi, "Burial Cave of the Caiaphas Family," *Biblical Archaeology Review*, September/October 1992, pp. 28-36, 76.

Greenhut, Zvi, "The 'Caiaphas' Tomb in North Talpiot, Jerusalem," *'Atiqot* (English Series) 21 (1992), pp. 63-71.

Greenhut, Zvi, "Discovery of the Caiaphas Family Tomb," *Jerusalem Perspective* 4/4-5 (1991), pp. 6-12.

Greenhut, Zvi, "Jerusalem—East Talpiot (Peace Forest)," *Archaeological News* 97 (1991), [in Hebrew], pp. 71-72.

Ilan, Tzvi, "Names of the Hasmoneans in the Second Temple Period," *Eretz Israel* 19 (1987), [in Hebrew], pp. 238-241.

Ilan, Tzvi, "Notes on the Distribution of Jewish Women's Names in Palestine in the Second Temple Period," *Journal of Jewish Studies* 40/2 (1989), pp. 191-192.

Josephus, Flavius, *Antiquities of the Jews* 18.35,95; 20.97-98,199-203.

Josephus, Flavius, *The Jewish War* 2.258-260.

Rahmani, L.Y., "Ancient Jerusalem's Funerary Customs and Tombs," *Biblical Archaeologist* 44/3 (1981), pp. 171-177; 44/4 (1981), pp. 229-235; 45/1 (1982), pp. 43-53; 45/2 (1982), pp. 109-119.

Reich, Ronny, "Caiaphas Name Inscribed on Bone Boxes," *Biblical Archaeology Review*, September/October 1992, pp. 38-44.

Reich, Ronny, "Jewish Burial Customs in the First Century," *Jerusalem Perspective* 4/4-5 (1991), p. 22.

Reich, Ronny, "Ossuary Inscriptions from the 'Caiaphas' Tomb," *'Atiqot* (English Series) 21, (1992), pp. 72-77.

Reich, Ronny, "Ossuary Inscriptions from the 'Caiaphas' Tomb," *Jerusalem Perspective* 4/4-5 (1991), pp. 13-21.

Zias, Joseph, "Human Skeletal Remains From the 'Caiaphas' Tomb," *'Atiqot* (English Series) 21 (1992), pp. 78-80.

PHOTO CREDITS

p. 14: Israel Museum/Nahum Slapak

p. 14: Drawing from Israel Museum Journal, vol. VIII

p. 15: Hershel Shanks (3)

P. 16: Eliyahu Dobkin Collection/Israel Museum/Erich Lessing (glass vase)

p. 17: Israel Antiquities Authority/Israel Museum/David Harris (kernos); Israel Museum (ceramic pomegranate);
Israel Antiquities Authority/Israel Museum (platter)

p. 18: Erich Lessing (Ugarit cult stand); Israel Museum/Nahum Slapak (Tel Nami cult stand and earrings)

p. 19: Vorderasiatisches Museum/Berlin (seal); American Numismatic Society (coin)

p. 20: Israel Museum/Nahum Slapak (Tel Nami scepters); Israel Antiquities Authority/Tsila Sagiv (Achziv scepters)

p. 21: Israel Antiquities Authority/Tsila Sagiv (Lachish scepters)

p. 22: Drawing courtesy Nahman Avigad

p. 24: Paleo-Hebrew alphabet by Larry G. Herr

p. 34: Garo Nalbandian

p. 36: David Harris

p. 37: Hershel Shanks

pp. 38-41: Israel Antiquities Authority

pp. 42-43: Adapted from *Jerusalem Perspective*

DATE DUE

THE LIBRARY STORE #47-0204